Potty Poets

DAD'S EXPLODING UNDERPANTS

With Thanks

To the very many bookshops across
the country who have helped to make
my previous revolting rhyme selections
such a great success!

Thanks, too, to Phil, Steve and Debbie
at The King's England Press for never
growing up!

DAD'S
EXPLODING
UNDERPANTS

And Other Potty Poems

by

Andrew Collett

Illustrated by Paddy Palgrave

𝕿𝖍𝖊 𝕶𝖎𝖓𝖌'𝖘 𝕰𝖓𝖌𝖑𝖆𝖓𝖉 𝕻𝖗𝖊𝖘𝖘
2000

ISBN 1 872438 45 8

Dad's Exploding Underpants is typeset by Moose Manuscripts
in Garamond 12pt and published by
The King's England Press Ltd,
Cambertown House, Commercial Road, Goldthorpe,
Rotherham, South Yorkshire, S63 9BL.

© Andrew Collett 2000
Illustrations ©Paddy Palgrave 2000
Fifth Impression, 2003

Printed and bound in Great Britain by
Woolnough Bookbinding
Irthlingborough
Northamptonshire

A Message From The Author

"It's only a joke book!
It's not real literature after all... we'll take two!"

I'm afraid that this book does not have a very nice title, but then this isn't meant to be a *nice* book! It's a revolting rhyme selection for older children. Of course, if you're a revolting adult then this is for you too! (Most adults are revolting - you can read about their horrible habits in this book!)

As with my first collection, entitled *Always Eat Your Bogies*, one of the reasons for writing this third book was to try and persuade reluctant readers to pick up a poetry selection. The same thinking was behind my second, *Bottling Burps for Grandma*. And so we carry on this tradition with *Dad's Exploding Underpants.*

As always, there will be some who'll argue that burps and bogies are not suitable subjects for poetry. Of course, if I'd called this a joke book then, just perhaps, the use of such revolting subject matter might be considered as more acceptable. Indeed, the above quotation comes from a lady I met recently at a book signing. She was quite unprepared to buy my first poetry book entitled *Always Eat Your Bogies*. However, when I suggested that children often viewed the poems merely as 'jokes', she smiled and bought two copies, reassured that I hadn't offended the sacred world of 'real' poetry. So, if my poems offend, then just imagine this as a joke book!

If you're still not convinced then I've always argued that it's better to have a child reading about bogies and burps than having that child not reading at all. Anyway, if a child has enjoyed one book, then there is every chance that he/she will want then to pick up another and another...

One last thing - this book is also about having fun! After all, reading should be FUN!

Dedications

To my son, Toby.

*For keeping me young in
thought and deed.*

To my wife, Deborah.

For understanding.

Dad's Exploding Underpants

Dad's exploding underpants
blow up every day,
so keep well down, don't look up,
try to run away.

For they're a deadly weapon,
out to make a stink
with their pretty patterns
and ribbons nice and pink.

But there's no bang or blast,
just a hissing sound,
as Dad's exploding underpants
lift him off the ground.

He flies into the sky,
not knowing which way to go,
with green and ghastly gases
blowing from below.

Then suddenly he stops,
he can't go any higher,
there's a horrible smell
as his bottom catches fire.

And so the show is over
as Dad finds a parachute
before coming down to earth
in half his birthday suit!

The Green Cross Code

When sitting at the traffic lights
with little to do,
this is the moment
drivers love to chew
anything they can find,
from gum to a sweet,
but, of course,
what they love to eat
is something that's green
and dribbles on their clothes,
for, when no one is looking,
they all pick their nose.

The Square Cow Pat

A cow one day out for a walk,
without so much as a care,
suddenly dropped a cow pat
in the shape of a square.

She stood and stared for a moment
to take in this strange sight
of a cow pat with four sides,
for she knew this couldn't be right.

Other cows quickly came over
to point at what lay on the ground,
for cow pats, if properly done,
they knew should always be round.

They started to laugh and to giggle,
they started to have some fun,
for they'd never seen a cow pat
which didn't dribble or run.

'I'm sorry,' the cow said quickly,
'it just came out that way,
it must be down to my diet
of one square meal each day!'

Our Foul Fridge

In our house the fridge
is never kept clean,
the marmalade is murky
and the yoghurts are green.

The milk has gone mouldy
with a nice yellow skin,
and there are spotty sausages
with a very strange grin.

There are bunions on onions
and salads with scum,
there are cheeses with sneezes
with noses that run.

There are pork pies in poor shape
being sick on the butter,
and leftovers now
lying dead in the gutter.

It's so very disgusting,
it's a terrible scene,
to see this foul fridge
which never looks clean.

Old Aged Bogey

A bogey quite old
will have seen better days,
it'll be crusty and brown
and set in its ways.

It'll be wrinkly and worn
and smelly beneath,
and old bogies will always
have rotten false teeth.

It'll be grumpy and cross
and covered in hair,
it'll splutter and cough
as it sits in its chair.

It'll be on its last legs
and smoking a pipe,
as it remembers the days
when it was juicy and ripe.

So do spare a thought
for bogies when beaten,
for they've lost all chance
of ever being eaten.

Boil Your Bum

Boil your bum,
do it for fun,
do it as quick as you can.

Stick in some sauce
and potatoes of course
in a great big bubbling pan.

Let it get hot,
in a big pot,
let it go steamy and red.

And you'll soon find
that your behind
starts to feel quite dead.

So, before it's too late,
give it a shake,
give it a bit of a splash.

Then run double-quick,
try not to slip
as you stick it in a cold bath.

A Message From Your Underpants

As you've not changed us
for at least a week,
I think it's time
for underpants to speak.

No longer will we
be treated this way,
we just don't want
another dirty day.

So come on underpants
across this town,
it's time for us
to wriggle right down.

Come on underpants
let's breathe fresh air,
and teach little boys
to change their underwear!

14

Dad's Nose Hair!

Keep down low!
Keep down low!
Dad's nose hair's
begun to grow.

It's oozing out
on full power
and growing in size
by the hour,
it's taking over
the whole street
and looking out
for things to eat,
it's worming
with bits of green,
for this nose hair
is looking mean,
it's biting things
as it goes
as it slops and slides
from Dad's nose.

So keep down low!
Keep down low!
Dad's nose hair's
begun to grow.

15

The Dentist's Chair

Grit your teeth,
don't be shy,
Mick the mechanic's
standing by.

For after serving
as an apprentice,
he's doubled-up -
as a dentist.

Watch him work
with real precision,
thinking through
each decision.

With dentist's drill
holding steady
and oily rag
at the ready.

He'll sort you out,
if you're willing,
with loads of grease
on each filling.

So open wide,
big and small,
be ready to gargle
engine oil.

So don't be shy,
don't be nervous,
just let big Mick
give you a service!

The Exploding Toilet

Our toilet keeps exploding,
it blows up twice a day,
shooting out the window
and landing miles away.

It spins into the air
like a rocket flying low,
dishing out dirty water
to everyone below.

But neighbours never mind,
they don't try to hide,
but queue up at our door
for a supersonic ride.

It's a real craze,
it's everyone's ambition,
to fly high on our toilet
on a supersonic mission.

So come on everybody,
do please take a spin,
get your hat and goggles,
come and jump straight in.

Come on everybody,
enjoy this great sensation
of flying on a toilet
high above our nation.

There's A Bum On The Run

There's a bum on the run,
everybody hide,
it's big and it's tall
and it's really quite wide.

It's bouncing down the road,
it's rolling round the block,
this bum on the run
just won't stop.

It's crunching and it's munching
everything in sight,
this bum on the run is
looking for a fight.

It's rolling and it's racing,
it's down every street,
with its funny looking face
and super-sized feet.

So watch out everybody,
keep well back,
for this bum on the run
might just attack!

Wriggly Round Hair

Wriggly round hair
found under you chair
has probably been left to rot.
So leave it alone,
don't take it home,
just stick it back into its spot.
One day it could be a clue
say, in the year 3002,
about how we spent our time -
leaving our hairs
under our chairs
to gather in mould and slime.

If Dinosaurs Were Alive

If we still had dinosaurs,
if they hadn't died away,
what would we do with those
still alive today?

Would they all be put to work
cleaning windows right up high?
Would a dinosaur have the job
of directing planes across the sky?

Would they all be bodyguards
for pop stars or the Queen?
Would they be demolition workers
instead of some machine?

Would they all be road builders
trampling tarmac into place?
Would they all launch satellites
high up into space?

So if we still had dinosaurs,
if they hadn't been swept away,
just what would we do with them
if they were alive today?

Fluff and Fingernails

Fluff under fingernails
is there for a reason,
so don't clean it out -
just let it season.

For fingernail fluff
is fertile and fun,
you'll be amazed
at what can be done.

Just leave it alone
for a month or more,
and it'll grow onions
which hang to the floor.

And then if you wait,
in under an hour
each fingernail will sprout
a cool cauliflower.

But if you want
things to go fast,
if you really want
your cauliflowers to last

Then drip on some dung,
make sure it lingers,
and then you'll have
some really green fingers!

My Dad's Underpants

Everyone stopped to glance
at my dad's underpants,
when I pinned them to our class wall.

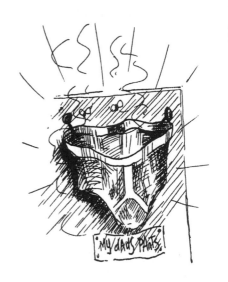

You see we'd been asked to bring
almost anything
to show, today, at school.

But my teacher went wild,
she called me a horrible child
she said that I was *so* bad.

And then she started to shout
and told me to get out
and go home to my old dad.

But before I could go,
as I think you may know,
a knock quickly came at the door.

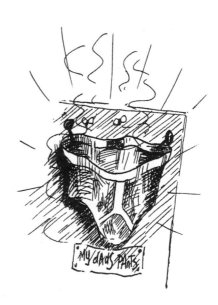

And there in the pink
near the painting sink
was my dad, stood in the raw.

'I'm sorry,' he cried,
trying to hide,
'but I need my underwear!

'You see, if you please,
they're my best undies
and I just don't have a spare.'

'Just take them away,
we haven't all day!'
said my teacher, not daring to look.

'OK,' said my dad,
feeling quite bad
and covering himself with a book.

But as he ran through the class
we all started to laugh
as Dad pulled his pants clear.

There wasn't anything he could do,
though hidden from view,
we still got a full face of his rear.

Kiss A Cow Pat

Kiss a cow pat,
don't be shy,
lick your lips
and have a try.

Kiss a cow pat
for a dare,
cow pats are found
everywhere.

Kiss a cow pat,
try a finger,
dip a toe,
let it linger.

Kiss a cow pat,
drop right in
and let it wriggle
on your skin.

Great Aunty Agnes

Great Aunty Agnes overloaded
the day when she suddenly exploded;
one minute she was in her chair
when suddenly the room was bare,
except for little bits of Aunt
clinging to a potted plant.

So how this happened we just don't know,
it seems a terrible way to go
but it feels as if she's still there,
sitting on her old armchair
for we seem to always discover
bits of Aunt under each cover!

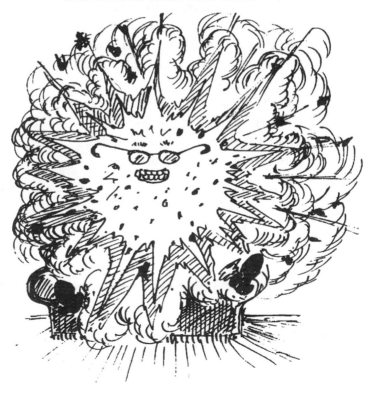

The Boiler House

When teacher told us a giant mouse
lived deep down in the boiler house,
we didn't believe her anyway,
but still we knew to keep away.

But Naughty Norma bit her lip
as she was planning a little trip
for Norma, though full ten years old,
never did as she was told.

And that same day, all too soon,
Norma was in the boiler room
ignoring the warnings of her teacher,
for she didn't believe in such a creature.

Then suddenly a terrible roar
sent her running for the door
where there was the tiniest gap
and, in the way, a human-trap.

Like a mouse-trap, but much bigger,
with a terrible and deadly trigger;
something from the Middle Ages -
the sort of stuff on history pages.

And then what really happened next
should be left to anyone's guess,
about the ending of one ten-year-old
who never did as she was told.

So if your teacher tells a tale
please, small people, do not fail,
listen hard, children do,
for her story might just be true!

A Loo In Love

To see if a loo loves you
just give it a flush,
and you'll tell in a moment
if it starts to blush.

You'll see its lid lilt
as its eyes start to roll,
and its tummy turn over
deep down in its bowl.

It will look away
if you sit on its seat,
and will never go out
for something to eat.

It will want to smell nice,
but only for you,
and take an interest
in all that you do.

So grab at that chain,
give it a shove,
and you'll soon know
if your loo's in love!

Our Cuckoo Clock

The cuckoo in our clock
must really be alive,
for every time it pops out,
we all have to dive,
we all have to hide
from a sudden drizzly shower,
for this tiny cuckoo clock
spends a penny on the hour.

Dad Lives In The Dustbin

Dad lives in the dustbin,
he says it's nice in there,
he's covered in old tissues
and has teabags in his hair.

There are mouldy bits of bacon
stuck between his teeth,
and cockroaches keep popping up
from somewhere down beneath.

Spaghetti left from yesterday
slips across his lips,
and nappies slowly empty
their nasty nappy bits.

But Dad still seems to like it,
he says he feels at home,
which is why Mum's now joined him
so he doesn't feel alone!

The Exploding Rabbit

A rabbit had a habit
of exploding by the hour,
it would go up with a bang
in a meteoric shower.

For this rabbit with a habit
did it just for fun,
to frighten off the farmer
with his nasty-looking gun.

Sweaty Socks

Sweaty socks
are always nice
boiled with bits
of rancid rice.

Suck them slowly,
let them drip,
tickle your taste buds
with a sip.

Stir them quickly
in your bowl
then open wide
and eat them whole!

AAAAARGH!!

Scared!

Here lies the body
of a small boy with braces
who liked to pull
the most horrible faces.

He died in an instant
still young and quite small,
when he scared himself silly
with the mirror in our hall.

Your Hairy Tummy

Hairs on your tummy
don't ever want to grow,
perhaps they're just plastic
and stuck on for show.

Wouldn't it be better
to have real ones instead,
then you'd have a tummy
just like your head.

Wouldn't it be great
to have a tummy with hair,
you could give it pigtails
to swing in the air.

Wouldn't it be super
to have a tummy with style
one you could show off
just once in a while.

So come on everybody,
take off your clothes,
to see if we can get
tummy hair that grows!

Munch On A Maggot

Maggots are amazing,
they're crunchy to the taste,
and with no bones or body
you get a better taste.

Once you've munched a maggot
you'll always want some more,
so gobble them with garnish,
eat them cooked or raw.

And for something different,
make that maggot squeal,
try picking up just one,
then slowly start to peel.

And if it's plump and fat,
if it's nice and fresh,
then you can just enjoy
the taste of maggot flesh.

So come on everybody,
enjoy this strange sensation,
for round and wriggly maggots
are the new food of our nation!

Crazy Christmas Families

Dad threw a pudding
at our TV screen,
two minutes before
the speech by our Queen.

When suddenly, before us,
in a wink of an eye,
Her picture popped up
to throw back a mince pie.

And then another,
with two more for luck,
Mum tried to run,
Dad tried to duck.

But it was already too late,
she'd got us in sight,
for all royal Queens
just love a good fight.

One pie exploded,
one hit my brother,
another hit Mum
as she ran for cover.

But the biggest of all
bounced off a chair
before smashing to bits
all over Dad's hair.

So let this be a lesson,
from Her Majesty the Queen,
don't ever throw puddings
at your TV screen.

Armpit Creatures

Armpits are full
of the most wonderful things,
like tiny white eggs
and creatures with wings.

Like slimy green slugs
gnawing beneath,
and biting bluebottles
with terrible teeth.

And if you don't believe
this to be true,
look in your armpit,
scrape off the goo.

And if you can look
closely enough,
you'll see these creatures
all doing their stuff!

The Turbo Tortoise

Most tortoises are slow,
about that there's little doubt,
but do not be surprised
if you should now find out
that one or two are different,
it really is quite true,
you might one day spot
a turbo-tortoise near to you.

They're faster than a rocket,
with stripes on every side,
and sometimes give small insects
a supersonic ride.
They're equipped with navigation
and satellite detection,
and when it comes to missiles
they have a great collection.

The even have full radar,
and boosters on their feet,
some come with parachutes
and a full ejector seat.
Some have cruise control
and infra-red night vision,
just so they can avoid
a turbo-tortoise collision.

So watch out in your garden
if your conifers start to quake,
if your vegetable patch disappears
and the ground begins to shake.
Watch out in your garden
if your flowers drop down dead,
for it'll be a turbo-tortoise
somewhere up ahead.

Shave Your Loo

Our toilet's in need
of a proper shave,
it's started to grow hairs
in different ways.

Some are so tiny
they creep round the bowl,
others are enormous
and could eat you up whole.

Some are so prickly
if you try for a seat,
they bite at your backside
as if you're something to eat.

Some are so springy
they catch on your clothes,
and others just jump
to tickle your nose.

So let's sort out it out,
let's give it a trim,
let's cut its hair
back to the rim.

So let's give our toilet
a brand-new face,
for we're tired of its hairs
all over the place.

Nose Hair Is Great!

Nose hair is great,
nose hair is fun,
you can twiddle and twist it
when your nose starts to run.

You can dye it or tie it
with particular ease,
you can save it all up
each time that you sneeze.

You can push it or pull it,
you can give it a lick,
you can break it and bend it
and of course - you can pick.

For nose hair is great,
it's a real treat,
and, if ever you're hungry,
it's super to eat!

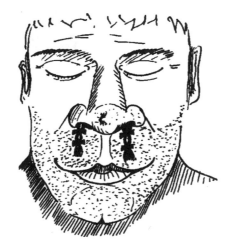

42

The Giant Underpants

Come on everybody,
keep well down,
for the giant underpants
are back in town.

They're out to take
your underwear,
you won't stand a chance
when they start to tear.

They'll take you too,
have no doubt,
for the giant underpants
will sniff you out.

So drop your underwear
to your feet,
and let the giant underpants
have it to eat.

Rabbit Droppings

Rabbit droppings
are small and round,
they're the best
to be found.

Compared with cats
and other creatures,
rabbit droppings
have little features.

I wonder how
they're made so well,
I wonder why
they never smell.

I wonder why
there's just one size,
for being quite perfect
they'd win a prize.

So let's celebrate
a rabbit's flair
at leaving droppings
in your chair.

Let's give thanks
that rabbit dung
doesn't drip
and doesn't run.

Let's enjoy,
oh let's do,
let's give thanks
for rabbit pooh.

Santa's Gone Potty

The reason Santa can tour the world
and still have time to spare
is because he's found a new machine
to shoot him through the air.

For even with two turbochargers
and rockets down each side,
Santa's tired-out Christmas sleigh
always gave a bumpy ride.

So it's hats off to Santa Claus
as he speeds throughout the night,
in his power-packed Santa potty,
painted pink and white.

For this potty comes with impact bars
and boosters round its bowl,
it even comes with radar
and potty cruise control.

This potty never needs to wait
it never needs to rest,
and for that little emergency
this potty's just the best.

So let's hear it for Santa Claus
with his potty pink and white,
speeding across the midnight sky
on every Christmas night.

Pimple Pie

Pimple pie is a recipe
that can be made almost for free:
just pour a pimple in a pan
and stir it up as fast as you can
then bring it quickly to the boil,
adding in some cooking oil
before whisking in some flaky flesh
to keep the pimple at its best,
then serve it with tomato sauce -
usually as a second course,
then you'll find that the flavour
is something to really savour!

Miss Jennifer Rose

Miss Jennifer Rose
would play her own nose
whenever there was a moment to spare.

She'd start to bop
playing classic or pop
with just one sniff in the air.

Her unusual vibrations
were the talk of all nations
for Jenny was famous you see.

She'd play special requests
for all paying guests
and the odd performance for charity.

She was all the rage
on telly and stage
for her nose really did suit her.

So let's stamp our feet
and join with the beat
of Jenny's happening hooter.

The Boy With
Two Bottoms

Having two bottoms
must seem like fun,
but just what do you do
with a spare bum?

You could draw on a face
and take it to a vet,
to see if people think
your bum is a pet.

You could tie it up high
so it hangs from your chin,
or hide it in a bum bag,
if it would fit in.

It could go in a pram,
there by your side,
so it looked like a baby
all wrinkly and wide.

But at the end of the day,
when all's said and done,
just what do you do
with a spare bum?

Smelly Welly Brother

My brother keeps his pack-up
in the bottom of his welly,
so when he sits down to lunch
his sandwiches are smelly.

But he doesn't seem to mind,
he eats them without waste,
for he says a smelly welly
gives his sandwich extra taste!

Don't Wash Those Socks!

Don't wash those socks,
that's what we say,
just keep them on
for another day!

Don't wash them both
in your machine,
you don't want socks
nice and clean.

Just keep them on,
wear them well,
wait until they
start to smell.

Keep them both
on your feet,
for at least
another week.

Then pull them off
double-quick,
peel away
their smelly grip.

Let them linger
nice and long,
enjoy the odour,
enjoy the pong.

So don't wash those socks,
that's what we say,
just keep them on
for another day!

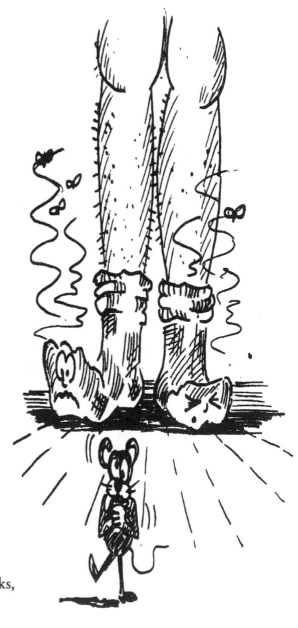

Mould In A Mug

Mould in a mug,
the two go together
like Laurel and Hardy,
like forecasts and weather.

Like bubble and squeak,
like Big Ben and time,
for mould and mugs
are partners in crime.

So don't throw it out,
don't let it go,
just let that mould
start to grow.

Wait till it creeps
right down the side,
wait for that mould
to grow green and wide.

Mould in a mug,
the two go together
like Laurel and Hardy,
like forecasts and weather.

Like bubble and squeak,
like Big Ben and time,
for mould and mugs
are partners in crime.

Underpants Can Dance

Underpants can dance,
watch them all boogie,
see them hit the floor
for they're really quite groovy.

Underpants can dance,
they'll wriggle and wave,
for bopping underpants.
are all the rave.

Underpants can dance,
so put them straight on,
and see if you can find
their favourite song.

My Room Is A Tip

My bedroom's untidy,
it's a real tip,
my mum says she's going
to throw my stuff in a skip.

She says there are cups
full of small creatures,
and bits of old corn flakes
with some really strange features.

She says there are socks
going green by day,
and underpants which
have started to stray.

She says it's disgusting,
she says it's a disgrace,
she says I should know better
and everything has a place.

To which I reply,
'I couldn't agree more,
everything has a place -
and that's on the floor.'

The Toilet Terminators

The toilet terminators
are back on the scene,
so make sure
your toilet is clean.

They're out to destroy
all dirty old loos,
they're armed and they're ready
as they march round in twos.

So freshen up your loo,
give it a wash,
pour in some perfume,
make it talk posh.

Give it a polish,
perhaps a new coat,
wash both its ears
and scrub down its throat.

For the toilet terminators
are back on the block,
so one day soon
you'll get the knock.

Be ready to show
your loo's spick and span,
let these terminators
sniff round your pan.

But if it's dirty,
if they find bits of goo,
if there's just one hair
inside your loo

They'll set it alight,
they'll blow-up your bowl,
leaving you with just
a dirty great hole.

So let this be a warning,
keep your loo fresh,
or it just might be given
the kiss of death!

The Bottom Snatchers

The bottom snatchers are out,
they're back on the scene,
they don't care if your bottom's
dirty or clean.

They'll chop it straight off,
you won't feel a thing,
except just a tickle
and a bit of a sting.

They work undercover,
dressed as old ladies,
or even young mothers
pushing small babies.

They're under orders
to kidnap your bottom,
for they're really mean
and ever so rotten.

So cover your backside,
give it a disguise,
paint on a face
or even some eyes.

Give it a new name,
send it on a trip,
just to give
the bottom-snatchers the slip!

Esmond's Bedroom

Esmond's bedroom couldn't be worse,
it's surely under some special curse
for it must be ten years or more
since last we saw his bedroom floor.

To say it's messy isn't the story;
the real one's much more gory,
so come right in, stay a while,
for it really is most gross and vile.

Wade right through old handkerchiefs
as they stick and pull at your knees,
but watch your step, do be bold,
for underneath live mugs of mould.

And mind the socks in a heap
for, under these, rats lie asleep,
and underpants, all aglow,
are left to wander down below.

So come on Esmond, why this tip?
Doesn't it ever make you sick?
Consider your wife, oh please do,
or is she just the same as you?

The King of Slime

I'm the king of slime,
can't you see,
that slime's good
for you and me.

I'm the king of slime,
don't you know,
I leave slime
wherever I go.

I'm the king of slime,
see what I mean,
I'm just one big
slime machine.

I'm the king of slime,
green and thick,
trying hard
to make you sick.

I'm the king of slime,
stand right back
I'm going to launch
a slime attack.

I'm the king of slime,
there it goes,
one thick blob
from my nose.

My Dad's Vest

My dad's mouldy old vest
is all he ever wears,
he gets the strangest of looks
and the wildest of stares.

It hangs to his feet
and is covered in grime,
but to take it off,
well he hasn't the time.

He's worn it at weddings
with top hat and tails,
and at scaring old ladies
his vest never fails.

It's his Sunday best
on each Christmas Day,
but at least it keeps
the relatives away.

For Dad's mouldy old vest
is his pride and joy,
for he hasn't taken it off
since he was a boy.

Dustbin-Lid-Sid

Dustbin-Lid-Sid
couldn't get rid
of his terrible rubbish-bin pong.

For he lived in the bottom
of something quite rotten -
a rubbish bin tall and quite long.

His clothes used to niff
with a terrible whiff
which would follow him down every street.

Like a pair of old pants
crawling with ants
mixed with mouldy old feet.

People would say
let's keep away
from Sid and his right rotten smell.

For it made people shout
and run about
as they started to feel unwell.

But Sid didn't mind,
he didn't think it unkind
that people kept out of his way.

Which is why he still lives in the bottom
of something quite rotten
to this very same day.

How Flies Find Cow Pats

When a cow drops a cow pat,
one that's big and round,
flies are quickly on red alert
before it hits the ground.

The airwaves begin to buzz,
for one channel is always kept clear,
so that flies can be told in an instant
if a fresh cow pat is suddenly near.

Even flies from across the border,
or those who don't normally stop,
are tuned into that special sound
of a cow suddenly doing a drop.

And as flies pull on their goggles
as they shoot above the town,
mission control radios information
about this cow pat big and brown.

Then with one last check for location
the flies close both their eyes,
as suddenly, in V formation,
they all begin to dive.

And with skill and real dedication,
with the target clearly in sight,
they crash into that succulent cow pat
with screams of sheer delight!

Dad Loves Old Food

Dad loves old food,
he really can't wait
to gobble anything
that's out of date.

Like bread with hair
or pizza with pimples,
even rice pudding
if it's covered in wrinkles.

Like sweaty spaghetti
or goulash gone grey,
and a crab with a scab
will really make his day.

For Dad loves old food,
he really can't wait
to gobble anything
that's out of date.

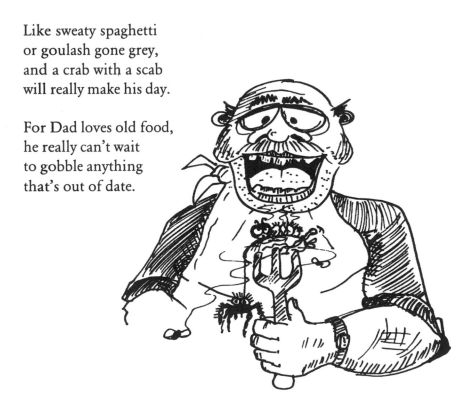

My Backside Has Teeth

My backside has teeth
deep down beneath,
they chomp and chew
day and night.

They'll eat anything at all
from a shed to a wall
as they munch and crunch
out of sight.

It's a bit of a riddle
to have in one's middle
a backside so terribly
ill-bred.

And it's beyond belief
that my front teeth
don't sit
inside my head.

But it could have been worse
if in total reverse
with my head
in place of my bottom.

For then I should spend every day
trying to keep away
from smells which are
really quite rotten.

Adders Can't Add

You've all heard the jokes
about an adder's ability
to add up hard sums
with amazing agility,
of course this is nonsense
of course this is mad,
adders can only divide,
they can't really add.

Faced with addition
an adder shakes its head,
turning this creature
a bright shade of red,
but make it divide
and the job's nearly done
for dividing is an adder's
idea of fun.

It'll work out the answer
without any fuss,
using its scales
like a long abacus,
pairing and sharing
as it lies on the floor
for a snake skin is what
dividing is for.

So perhaps if the adder
had a new name,
one which was suited
to the dividing game,
then such snakes
wouldn't be driven mad
with those ridiculous tales
of how they can add.

Grandad's Buttons

They're a secret weapon
on red alert,
so watch those buttons
on Grandad's shirt.

For he's had dinner,
he's eaten the lot,
and now those buttons
are a deadly shot.

So hit the floor,
fear the worst,
Grandad's shirt's
about to burst.

Don't look up,
don't ask why,
watch those buttons
start to fly.

There they go
like a rocket,
from his middle
and each pocket.

There they shoot
to the door
and his tummy tumbles
to the floor.

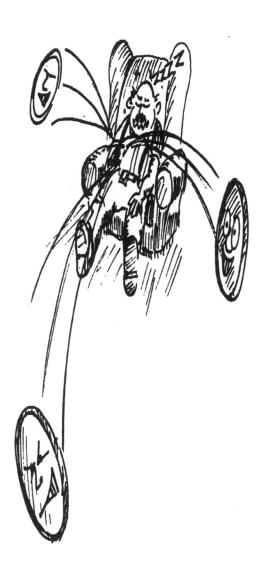

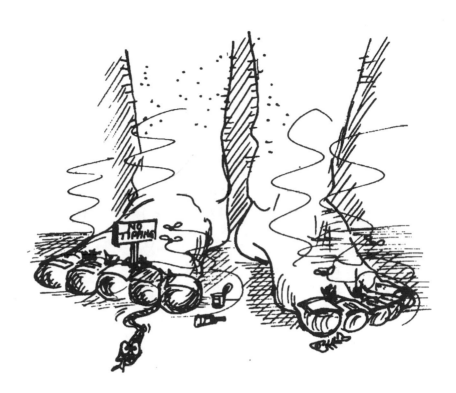

The Gunge

Gouge out the gunge
between your toes,
pick it and peel it
then line it in rows.

Jam it and cram it
into piles of two,
then pick up a piece
and give it a chew.

The Prince-Frog

There was once a fairytale,
they've been many others since,
of a frog who was kissed
and then turned into a prince

Which might sound inviting,
it might sound quite cosy,
it might paint a picture
of an ending that's rosy.

But don't be delighted,
don't think this fun,
don't think this story
will run and run.

For the truth is much simpler,
but not widely known,
for this prince never wanted
to be in line to the throne.

And so, after this kiss,
being a selfish chap,
he went out with his friends
and never came back.

He left a little note
stuck under a log
explaining how much
he'd liked being a frog.

He said that settling down
wasn't his kind of thing,
even though he might
one day be King.

He said that she was free
and his word was his bond,
and with that our frog-prince
hopped back to his pond.

Greedy Little Nigel

Little Nigel kept his toys
away from other girls and boys,
for there's one thing he wouldn't do
and that's to share with me or you.

When other children came his way
to talk or even try and play,
Little Nigel would pull a sneer
so as to make the message clear.

He even had a wooden box
complete with automatic locks
so all his toys, there to see,
were hidden under lock and key.

But things went wrong late one night
giving Nigel a terrible fright,
for as he tried to get undressed
he fell into this wooden chest.

Automatic locks all snapped tight
as Nigel's face turned quite white,
leaving him to scream and shout
for he knew of no way out.

Of course others heard the call
from that boy, very small,
but they knew to keep away
from selfish boys who wouldn't play.

And so poor Nigel, all alone,
with just a box for his home,
was to never again to see his toys,
or any other girls or boys.

If Your Toilet Could Talk

If your toilet could talk
just what would it say?
Would it ask for a wash
at least twice a day?

Would it make a request
that you go on a diet?
Just to give this poor toilet
a little peace and quiet.

Would it make a suggestion
for a better view?
For there's not much to look at
if you're just a loo.

Would it perhaps
want floodlights below?
So it's not in the dark
each time that you go.

And what would it sound like?
Would it be shy?
Would it call out rude names
when people walked by?

Would it pull silly faces
and spit from beneath?
And would this toilet
also have teeth?

So I wonder what a toilet
would want to say,
if ever it could talk
for only one day?

Today's Hammer-head Sharks

Today's young hammer-heads
come with battery power,
so they can charge themselves up
in less than an hour.

For gone is that hammer-head
which never looked cool,
no, hammer-heads now come
with every available tool.

Some with power screwdrivers
for real DIY,
others with blades
just to make things fly.

Some have big drills
which spin in the air,
to give ships and small vessels
a bit of a scare.

But when they're not fighting,
when they're being good,
you'll be surprised what a hammer-head
can now make from wood.

For when on the sea bed
you can hear the noise
of the young hammer-heads
playing with their new power toys.

Making chairs and fine tables
and frames with a border,
in fact, anything at all -
should you care to order.

For these young hammer-heads
love the deafening roar
of their new power tools
when on the sea floor.

Where to Find Andrew's Material

The following anthologies contain some of Andrew's work:

Oxford University Press: *A Purple Poetry Paintbox, Legends Poems, Mystery Poems, Excuses Excuses, Magic Poems, Wordwhirls, Teacher Teacher, This Is Mum, Oxford Anthology 3, I'm In A Mood & Football Fever.*

Macmillan: *We Was Robbed, More Secret Lives of Teachers, Aliens Stole My Underpants, While Shepherds Washed Their Socks, Revenge of The Man-Eating Gerbils, They Think It's All Over, School Trip Poems, Unzip Your Lips, I'm Telling On You, Mini Beast Poems, Teacher's Pets, Unzip Your Lips Again, Marvellous Machines, Spectacular Spooks, Wacky Wild Animals, Hysterical Historical Poems: The Romans, The Tudors & The Victorians.*

Wayland: *Space Poems, The Upside-Down Frown, Poems About Me, Poems About You & Me.*

Scholastic: *Young Hippo Magic Poems, Young Hippo School Poems & Young Hippo Animal Poems.*

Ginn: *Sugarcake Bubble, Countdown,* and *Hop to The Sky.*

Early Learning Centre: *Revolting Songs and Poems, Paws and Claws* and *Food Glorious Food.*

Other: **Hodder** - *A Time Capsule of Poems.* **Bloomsbury** - *I Wanna Be Your Mate.* **Pearson Educational** - *Tongue Twisters, Limericks & Humorous Verse.* **Barefoot Books** - *Someone I Like.* **Evans** - *Footsteps On The Page.* **Stanley Thornes** - *Hot Heads, Warm Hearts, Cold Streets.* **Heinemann** - *Something In The Cupboard* & short story in *Literacy World Anthology, Stage One.* **Folens** - various poetry posters. **Playhouse Cassettes** - *How Much Is That Doggie?*

Complete Collections:

CRS Records - *The Magic Christmas Tree.* Forty minutes of poetry and stories read and written by Andrew.
King's England Press - *Always Eat Your Bogies, Bottling Burps for Grandma,* and *Electric Knickers.*
Ginn - *Smugglers.* A Short novel from Andrew.